Small French Paintings

FROM THE BEQUEST OF AILSA MELLON BRUCE

National Gallery of Art, Washington

This catalogue was written by David E. Rust and was produced by the Editor's Office, National Gallery of Art, Washington. Printed by Stephenson Incorporated, Washington, D.C. Set in Weiss by Waldman Graphics, Inc., Philadelphia, Pennsylvania. The text paper is eighty-pound Warren's Patina and the cover is eighty-pound LOE dull. Designed by Melanie B. Ness

Library of Congress Cataloging in Publication Data:

United States.   National Gallery of Art.
    Small French Paintings from the Bequest of
Ailsa Mellon Bruce.

    Bibliography: p. XVI

    1.   Painting, French—Exhibitions.   2.   Impressionism (Art)—France—Exhibitions.   3.   Post-impressionism (Art)—France—Exhibitions.
4.   Painting, Modern—19th century—France—
Exhibitions.   5.   Bruce, Ailsa Mellon—Art collections—Exhibitions.   I.   Title.
ND547.5.I4U6   1978a   759.4′074′0153   78-606019

Exhibition opened at the National Gallery of Art, East Building, on June 1, 1978.

COVER AND TITLE PAGE: **Berthe Morisot** *Harbor at Lorient* (detail)

Contents

Preface   VII

Introduction   XI

Author's acknowledgments   XV

List of abbreviations   XVII

The catalogue   1

Index of artists   121

Pierre Bonnard *Two Dogs in a Deserted Street*

Preface

by J. Carter Brown
Director

Ailsa Mellon Bruce did not live to see the opening of the East Building of the National Gallery of Art, a project which she in such large measure has made possible, even as her father did not live to see the opening of the Gallery's original building, which he gave.

In her lifetime, Mrs. Bruce maintained a keen interest in the Gallery. Working closely with the then-director, John Walker, she personally underwrote many of the Gallery's major acquisitions. In addition, in equal share with the donations of her brother, the president of the Gallery, Paul Mellon, her personal generosity made it possible for the Gallery to embark on its expansion project. The final third of that funding has been provided by the Andrew W. Mellon Foundation, which she and her brother created, and to which she bequeathed the bulk of her estate. This nation can be grateful to the trustees of that foundation for continuing to share her interest in this institution.

We can also rejoice in the additional good fortune that Mrs. Bruce bequeathed her entire collection of paintings to the National Gallery of Art. Some of these magnificent works of art are already on view in the West Building, including the great Goya *Condesa de Chinchón*, and many of her larger-scale impressionist and post-impressionist paintings, such as the large and great Monet, *The Artist's Garden at Vétheuil*, or the late Cézanne landscape, *Riverbank*.

Many of her best-loved pictures, however, are of such intimate, domestic scale that they cannot be exhibited to advantage in the existing galleries of the West Building. Eventually, the move of many of the behind-the-scenes functions of the Gallery to newly created spaces in the expansion project will release space in the West Building so that new galleries can be constructed to adjoin those on the West Building's main floor that are already devoted to French impressionist and post-impressionist painting.

Meanwhile, the East Building of the National Gallery has been designed to provide exhibition facilities for works of art of all scales. For its opening, therefore, it has seemed appropriate that the Gallery put on view these delightful works of art, whose appeal, when exhibited in sympathetic spaces, is in no way diminished by their small format.

Thus, this little exhibition is designed to accomplish several things at once. It should, first of all, provide a source of visual delight by putting on view material that the Gallery has been

Eugène Boudin *Yacht Basin at Trouville-Deauville*

heretofore unable to exhibit. In addition, for the opening of the East Building, which itself must be considered one of the opening exhibits, it illustrates the range of capability that the architecture provides. And finally, this selection can serve to represent Mrs. Bruce, and her deep feeling for art, at a moment which she unfortunately was not able to experience firsthand.

Auguste Renoir *Madame Monet and Her Son*

Introduction

by John Rewald

The French paintings of the nineteenth and early twentieth centuries which Ailsa Mellon Bruce bequeathed to the National Gallery can be divided into two distinct groups. One is composed of the Edward Molyneux Collection, which Mrs. Bruce bought in 1955 upon the advice of John Walker, then chief curator of the National Gallery, where the collection had been shown in 1952; the other is made up of ten paintings acquired for her own collection between 1930 and 1955, as well as subsequent individual purchases that added significantly to the Molyneux Collection. The small paintings which form the present exhibit are a selection of French impressionist and post-impressionist paintings from this bequest.

The peculiar charm of the Molyneux Collection was that it concentrated on works of a small and intimate scale. While this was not too difficult where Seurat panels, studies by Boudin, or early Bonnard or Vuillard paintings were concerned, it was an achievement to have discovered a tiny Manet still life that, despite its size, shows a tremendous freedom of brushwork; a minuscule—though explosively colorful—fauve Matisse; or a delicate little painting by Toulouse-Lautrec. Though Molyneux had a predilection for these small canvases in which spontaneity is unbridled and where the painter seems to have abandoned himself exclusively to his own pleasure, his quest for exquisiteness was not hampered by rigors of scale. The guiding factor was exceptional quality. Thus, his collection featured two of the most sensitive and charming canvases by Berthe Morisot, a splendid early Monet representing—in his still somewhat dry manner—his mistress Camille with his friend Frédéric Bazille, a delicate and misty street scene by Sisley, Renoir's delightful picture of Madame Monet with her son in their garden in Argenteuil, and van Gogh's sun-drenched landscape of Provence.

When the Molyneux pictures were shown at the Museum of Modern Art in New York after their exhibition in Washington, the author of the preface to the catalogue commented that the collector, "leaving the full power of big orchestras to museums . . . had surrounded his daily life with the loveliest chamber music created during the last hundred years." Yet when this ensemble passed on to Mrs. Mellon Bruce, she decided to expand it, since she planned to follow her father's example and leave her paintings to the National Gallery. Thus, she eliminated a few works from the Molyneux Collection, mostly by twentieth-century artists, and little by little added a number of outstanding canvases, which, in the most felicitous way, complement the original group. A major work by Corot lends weight to his

Edouard Manet *Flowers in a Crystal Vase*

presence; several excellent paintings by Pissarro give this artist an outstanding representation; two important oils by Monet illustrate the evolution of this master; more emphasis was given to Manet, Sisley, Renoir, and Bonnard; and works by Cézanne and Cassatt entered the collection.

Rather than distract from the initial collection, these acquisitions complete it. They provide a balance between small, exquisite treasures on the one hand, and large, significant pieces on the other. At the same time they establish a balance between the unusually fine, original representation of Berthe Morisot, for instance, and that of her fellow impressionists, most of whom were not included with similarly important works. The result is a cohesive and exceptional group. Although there is no way of telling how Mrs. Mellon Bruce may have further extended her collection had she lived, it constitutes, as she left it, a welcome and precious addition to the National Gallery, for which she had already done so much.

Claude Monet *Ships Riding on the Seine at Rouen*

Author's acknowledgments

by David E. Rust
Curator of French Painting

There have been countless people who have been extremely helpful in the preparation of this catalogue. Those who contributed most were John Rewald and Giorgio Galansino, and we are more than grateful to them for their advice and preliminary cataloguing. Charles Durand-Ruel, François Daulte, Robert Schmit and Antoine Salomon also deserve special recognition for their expertise and research, so generously shared. Nancy Troy, who was one of the Gallery's summer interns, is another deserving of special thanks, as are many on the staff of the Gallery's library.

Among the multitude of others who have been helpful, and to whom I should like to express our gratitude are: Pierre Angrand, Janine Bailly-Herzberg, Anne Marie Bergeret, Adelyn Breeskin, Harry Brooks, Klaus Bussmann, Ralph T. Coe, Douglas Cooper, Desmond Corcoran, Peter Davidock, Jean Devoisins, the late Jean Dieterle, Jean Dauberville, Mauricette Fallek, Alix de Fontenay, Peter Gimpel, John Gordon, Gilbert Gruet, Delbert R. Gutridge, Anne Coffin Hanson, Robert L. Herbert, Ay-Whang Hsia, J. M. Joosten, Magne Malmanger, J. Patrice Marandel, Teresa Newman, David T. Owsley, Paul Pétridès, Nils Eger Pettersen, John Richardson, Madeleine Rocher-Jauneau, Alexandre Rosenberg, Denis Rouart, Rita Salfeld, Grace Seiberling, Robert Shadforth, Mildred Steinbach, Patricia Swain, Antoine Terrasse, Nicholas A. Tooth, M. van der Ven, Anne M. Wagner, Rodolph Walter, E. L. L. de Wilde, Daniel Wildenstein, W. W. Wissman, and Nancy Wixom.

Edouard Vuillard *Child Wearing a Red Scarf*

List of Abbreviations

Molyneux 1952: Washington, D.C., National Gallery of Art, and New York, Museum of Modern Art, "French Paintings from the Molyneux Collection," 1952.

EXHIBITIONS

Palm Beach 1958: Palm Beach, Florida, The Society of the Four Arts, "Paintings by Claude Monet; Paintings from the Collection of Mrs. Mellon Bruce," 1958.

San Francisco 1961: San Francisco, California Palace of the Legion of Honor, "French Paintings of the Nineteenth Century from the Collection of Mrs. Mellon Bruce," 1961.

NGA 1966: Washington, D.C., National Gallery of Art, "French Paintings from the Collection of Mr. and Mrs. Paul Mellon and Mrs. Mellon Bruce; Twenty-fifth Anniversary Exhibition, 1941-1966," 1966.

BIBLIOGRAPHY

NGA 1975: National Gallery of Art, *European Paintings: an Illustrated Summary Catalogue*, Washington, D.C., 1975.

Walker 1975: J. Walker, *National Gallery of Art, Washington*, New York, 1975.

Kelder 1977: D. Kelder, *French Impressionist Masterpieces*, New York, 1977.

Georges Seurat *Study for "La Grande Jatte"*

This catalogue is organized chronologically by birthdates of artists.

Jean-Baptiste-Camille Corot, 1796-1875

River Scene with Bridge, 1834

Canvas, 0.250 x 0.338 (9⅞ x 13⅜ in.)
Inscribed at lower left: *Corot Pingebat 1834;*
Falsely inscribed at lower left: *Corot 1834*
2394

Provenance: Edward Molyneux, Paris; Ailsa Mellon Bruce, New York, 1955.

Exhibitions: Molyneux 1952, repr.; San Francisco 1961, no. 15, repr.; NGA 1966, no. 1, color repr.

Bibliography: A. Schoeller and J. Dieterle, *Corot,* Deuxième Supplément à "L'Oeuvre de Corot" par. A. Robaut et E. Moreau-Nélaton, Paris, 1956, no. 9, repr.; R. Goldwater, "The Glory that was France," *Art News* 55, no. 1 (Mar., 1966): p. 40, repr. (color) p. 44; M.S. Young, "The Mellon Collections: The Great Years of French Painting," *Apollo* 83 (June, 1966): 426-27, repr. p. 427, fig. 2; NGA 1975, p. 78, no. 2394, repr. p. 79; Walker 1975, repr. (color) p. 433, no. 626.

Jean-Baptiste-Camille Corot, 1796-1875

Beach near Etretat, 1872

Canvas, 0.125 x 0.255 (4⅞ x 10 in.)
Inscribed at lower left: COROT
2489

Provenance: F. Stumpf, Paris (sale, Paris, Hôtel Drouot, Nov. 27, 1894, no. 19); Tempelaere; Aimé Diot, Paris (sale, Paris, Hôtel Drouot, Mar. 8-9, 1897, no. 35); Hazard (sale, Paris, Georges Petit, Dec. 3, 1919, no. 91); Rosenthal, Paris (sale, Paris, May 9, 1934, no. 67); Dr. G. Viau; Baron Pellenc, Paris, 1944; André Schoeller, Paris, 1945; Edward Molyneux, Paris; Ailsa Mellon Bruce, New York, 1955.

Exhibitions: Molyneux 1952; Palm Beach 1958, no. 26; San Francisco 1961, no. 14, repr.

Bibliography: A. Robaut, *L'Oeuvre de Corot,* vol. 3, Paris, 1905, p. 270, no. 2076, repr. p. 271; NGA 1975, p. 80, no. 2489, repr. p. 81.

Eugène Boudin, 1824-1898

Beach at Trouville, 1864/65

Wood, 0.259 x 0.479 (10¼ x 18⅞ in.)
Inscribed at lower right: *E. Boudin.*
2384

Provenance: Dieterle, Paris; Paul Gerson, New York; Viscount Rothermere
(sale, London, Christie's, Dec. 19, 1941, no. 34); Edward Molyneux, Paris;
Ailsa Mellon Bruce, New York, 1955.

Exhibitions: London, National Gallery, "Nineteenth Century Paintings," 1943,
no. 68; Molyneux 1952; NGA 1966, no. 16, repr.

Bibliography: R. Schmit, *Eugène Boudin*, vol. 1, Paris, 1973, p. 112, no. 318,
repr.; NGA 1975, p. 42, no. 2384, repr. p. 43; Walker 1975, repr. (color)
p. 447, no. 646.

Eugène Boudin, 1824-1898

On the Jetty, c. 1869/70

Wood, 0.184 x 0.273 (7¼ x 10¾ in.)
Falsely inscribed at lower right: *E. Boudin 1870* [?]
2385

Provenance: Paris, Hôtel Drouot, Nov. 28, 1949, no. 80, pl. IX; E. Slater, London; Reid & Lefevre, London, 1950; Edward Molyneux, Paris, 1951; Ailsa Mellon Bruce, New York, 1955.

Exhibitions: Molyneux 1952.

Bibliography: R. Schmit, *Eugène Boudin*, vol. 1, Paris, 1973, p. 160, no. 430, repr.; NGA 1975, p. 42, no. 2385, repr. p. 43; Walker 1975, repr. (color) p. 446, no. 644.

Eugène Boudin, 1824-1898

The Beach, 1877

Wood, 0.109 x 0.254 (4¼ x 10 in.)
Inscribed at lower left: *E. Boudin;* lower right: *Tlle* 77
2386

Provenance: Viscount Rothermere, London (sale, London, Christie's, Dec. 19, 1941, no. 37); Tooth, London; Edward Molyneux, Paris; Ailsa Mellon Bruce, New York, 1955.

Exhibition: London, National Gallery, "Nineteenth Century French Paintings," 1941, no. 31; Molyneux 1952; San Francisco 1961, no. 7, repr.; NGA 1966, no. 18, repr.

Bibliography: R. Schmit, *Eugène Boudin*, vol. 1, Paris, 1973, p. 224, no. 618, repr.; NGA 1975, p. 42, no. 2386, repr. p. 43; Walker 1975, repr. (color) p. 446, no. 643.

Eugène Boudin, 1824-1898

Women on the Beach at Berck, 1881

Wood, 0.248 x 0.362 (9¾ x 14¼ in.)
Inscribed at lower left: *E. Boudin. 81/Berck*
2387

Provenance: Adolphe Tavernier, Paris (sale, Paris, Hôtel Drouot, Mar. 23, 1903, no. 14); Anonymous sale, London, Christie's, June 23, 1906, no. 44; Bernheim-Jeune, Paris, 1906; Jacques Lindon, New York; Ailsa Mellon Bruce, New York, 1947.

Bibliography: R. Schmit, *Eugène Boudin,* vol. 2, Paris, 1973, p. 90, no. 1510, repr.; NGA 1975, p. 42, no. 2387, repr. p. 43; Walker 1975, repr. (color) p. 447, no. 648.

Eugène Boudin, 1824-1898

Yacht Basin at Trouville-Deauville, probably 1895/96

Wood, 0.458 x 0.371 (18 x 14⅝ in.)
Atelier stamp at lower right: *E. Boudin*
2388

Provenance: Atelier Eugène Boudin (sale, Paris, Hôtel Drouot, Mar. 20-21, 1899, no. 93); Levaique, Paris; Wildenstein, New York; Ailsa Mellon Bruce, New York, 1966.

Bibliography: R. Schmit, *Eugène Boudin,* vol. 3, Paris, 1973, p. 165, no. 3019, repr.; NGA 1975, p. 42, no. 2388, repr. p. 43; Walker 1975, repr. (color) p. 447, no. 649.

Eugène Boudin, 1824-1898

Washerwomen on the Beach of Etretat, 1894

Wood, 0.372 x 0.549 (14⅝ x 21⅝ in.)
Inscribed at lower left: *E. Boudin 94*; lower right: *Etretat*.
2389

Provenance: Georges Ibos, Paris (sale, Paris, Hôtel Drouot, June 19, 1900, no. 11, repr.); Durand-Ruel, Paris; Van Wisselingh, Amsterdam, 1935; M.P. Voûte, Jr., Amsterdam; Van Wisselingh, Amsterdam, 1937; Knoedler, New York, 1937; Harry MacNeill Bland, New York, 1942; Ailsa Mellon Bruce, New York.

Exhibitions: Amsterdam, Van Wisselingh, "Tentoonstelling Eugène Boudin, 1824-1898," 1937, no. 24.

Bibliography: R. Schmit, *Eugène Boudin*, vol. 3, Paris, 1973, p. 239, no. 3229, repr.; NGA 1975, p. 42, no. 2389, repr. p. 43; Walker 1975, repr. (color) p. 446, no. 645.

Camille Pissarro, 1830-1903

Orchard in Bloom, Louveciennes, 1872

Canvas, 0.450 x 0.550 (17¾ x 21⅝ in.)
Inscribed at lower right: *C. Pissarro. 1872*
2423

Provenance: Durand-Ruel, Paris, 1872; Alfred Bernheim, Paris; Durand-Ruel, Paris; Sam Salz, New York; Ailsa Mellon Bruce, New York, 1960.

Exhibitions: Paris, Nadar, "Première exposition, Société anonyme des artistes peintres, sculpteurs, graveurs," 1874, probably no. 136 (*Le Verger*); Paris, Marcel Bernheim, "Les Premières époques de Camille Pissarro, de 1858 à 1884," 1936, no. 13; San Francisco 1961, no. 37, repr.; NGA 1966, no. 27, repr.

Bibliography: Galerie Durand-Ruel, *Recueil d'estampes gravées à l'eau forte*, vol. 1, Paris, 1873, pl. 46, repr. in etching by Greux; L. R. Pissarro and L. Venturi, *Camille Pissarro, son art, son oeuvre*, vol. 1, Paris, 1939, p. 100, no. 153; vol 2, pl. 131; J. Rewald, *The History of Impressionism*, New York, 1961, 1973, repr. (color) p. 297; J. Rewald, "The Impressionist Brush," *The Metropolitan Museum of Art Bulletin* 32, no. 3 (1973/74), no. 14, repr. (color detail); R. Cogniat, *Pissarro*, Paris, 1974, repr. (color) p. 19; H. Adhémar and S. Gache, "L'Exposition de 1874 chez Nadar," *Centenaire de l'Impressionisme*, Paris, 1974, p. 249f., no. 136, repr. p. 249; NGA 1975, p. 270, no. 2423, repr. p. 271; Walker 1975, repr. (color) p. 513, no. 769; Kelder 1977, p. 40, repr. (color) p. 41.

Edouard Manet, 1832-1883

A King Charles Spaniel, c. 1866

Canvas, 0.464 x 0.382 (18¼ x 15 in.)
Inscribed at lower right: *éd. Manet*
2408

Provenance: Leclanché, Paris; Bernheim-Jeune, Paris, 1910; Dr. Julius Elias, Berlin, 1910; Eilif Moe, Lillehammer, Norway, 1946; Wildenstein, New York, 1949; Ailsa Mellon Bruce, 1958.

Exhibitions: Paris, "Exposition Manet," 1867, no. 42; Berlin, Galerie Matthiesen, "Austellung Edouard Manet, 1832-1883," 1928, no. 17, pl. XV; Oslo, Kunstnernes Hus, "Fransk Utstilling," 1946, no. 11; Washington, D.C., National Gallery of Art, "Masterpieces of French Impressionist and Post-Impressionist Painting," 1959, p. 14, repr.; NGA 1966, no. 38, repr.

Bibliography: T. Duret, *Histoire de Manet et de son oeuvre,* Paris, 1902, pp. 214-215, and successive editions, no. 89; E. Moreau-Nélaton, Manuscript catalogue of Manet's oeuvre, Paris, 1906, no. 99; T. Duret, *Manet and the French Impressionists,* London and Philadelphia, 1910, p. 223, no. 89; E. Moreau-Nélaton, *Manet raconté par lui-même,* vol. 1, Paris, 1926, pp. 86n, 89, fig. 96; A. Tabarant, *Manet-histoire catalographique,* Paris, 1931, p. 159, no. 118; P. Jamot, G. Wildenstein, and M. T. Bataille, *Manet,* vol. 1, Paris, 1932, p. 132, no. 128, vol. 2, repr. p. 171, fig. 348; R. Rey, *Manet,* Paris and New York, 1938, p. 163, no. 150, repr. p. 150; A. Tabarant, *Manet et ses oeuvres,* Paris, 1947, pp. 131, 606, no. 129, repr.; D. Rouart and S. Orienti, *Edouard Manet,* Paris, 1970, p. 96, no. 112, fig. 112; S. Orienti, *The Complete Paintings of Manet,* London, 1970 (Italian edition, 1967), p. 97, no. 113A, repr. p. 96; G. Bazin, *Edouard Manet,* Milan, 1972, and Paris, 1974, p. 33, repr. (color); D. Rouart and D. Wildenstein, *Edouard Manet, Catalogue raisonné,* vol. 1, Lausanne-Paris, 1975, p. 194, no. 233, repr. p. 1º5; NGA 1975, p. 212, no. 2408, repr. p. 213; Walker 1975, repr. (color) p. 453, no. 662.

Edouard Manet, 1832-1883

Flowers in a Crystal Vase, c.1882

Canvas, 0.326 x 0.243 (12⅞ x 9⅝ in.)
Inscribed at lower right: *Manet*
2409

Provenance: Gift of the artist to Madame X; Madame Jules Féral, Paris;
Edward Molyneux, Paris; Ailsa Mellon Bruce, New York, 1955.

Exhibitions: London, Royal Academy of Arts, "Exhibition of French Art, 1200-
1900," 1932, p. 252, no. 561; Paris, Musée de l'Orangerie, "Exposition
Manet, 1832-1883," 1932, no. 87a (not in catalogue); Amsterdam,
J. Goudstikker, "Het Stilleven," 1933, no. 206, repr. no. 66; Rotterdam,
Museum Boymans, "Tentoonstelling van 115 Stillevens 1480-1933," 1933,
no. 60; Amsterdam, Stedelijk Museum, "Honderd Jaar Fransche Kunst,"
1938, no. 162; Paris, Charpentier, "Natures mortes françaises du XVIIᵉ siècle à
nos jours," 1951, no. 105 repr.; Molyneux 1952; San Francisco 1961,
no. 24, repr.; NGA 1966, no. 45, repr.

Bibliography: Matthiesen, *Austellung Edouard Manet, 1832-1883*, Berlin, 1928,
no. 84 (not shown); A. Tabarant, *Manet, histoire catalographique*, Paris, 1931,
no. 406; P. Jamot, G. Wildenstein, and M. T. Bataille, *Manet*, vol. 1, Paris,
1932, p. 180, no. 508, vol. 2, fig. 385; R. Rey, *Manet*, Paris and New York,
1938, p. 163, no. 153, repr. (color) p. 153; A. Tabarant, *Manet et ses oeuvres*,
Paris, 1947, repr. p. 616, no. 437; D. Rouart and S. Orienti, *Edouard Manet*,
Paris, 1970, p. 120, no. 417H, repr. p. 121, fig. 417H; S. Orienti, *The
Complete Paintings of Manet*, London, 1970 (Italian edition, 1967), p. 120,
no. 411H, repr. p. 121, fig. 411H; D. Rouart and D. Wildenstein, *Edouard
Manet, Catalogue raisonné*, vol. 1, Lausanne-Paris, 1975, p. 302, no. 420, repr.
p. 303; NGA 1975, p. 212, no. 2409, repr. p. 213; Walker 1975, repr.
(color) p. 457, no. 667; Kelder 1977, p. 10, repr. (color) p. 11.

Edgar Degas, 1834-1917

Dancers Backstage, c.1890

Canvas, 0.242 x 0.188 (9½ x 7⅜ in.)
Inscribed at upper right: *Degas*
2397

Provenance: Théodore Duret, Paris (sale, Paris, Georges Petit, Mar. 16, 1894, no. 12); Durand-Ruel, Paris; Reid & Lefevre, London, 1928; Carroll Carstairs, New York; Ailsa Mellon Bruce, New York, 1948.

Exhibitions: New York, Wildenstein, "A Loan Exhibition of Degas," 1949, no. 78, repr. p. 56; San Francisco 1966, no. 18, repr.; NGA 1966, no. 61, repr.

Bibliography: P. A. Lemoisne, *Degas et son oeuvre,* vol. 3, Paris, 1946, p. 596, no. 1024, repr. p. 597; L. Browse, *Degas Dancers,* London, 1949, p. 394, no. 175, repr.; F. Russoli and F. Minervino, *L'Opera complete di Degas,* Milan, 1970, p. 125, no. 859, repr.; NGA 1975, p. 100, no. 2397, repr. p. 101; Walker 1975, repr. (color) p. 483, no. 719.

Edgar Degas, 1834-1917

Dancers at the Old Opera House, c.1877

Pastel, 0.218 x 0.171 (8⅝ x 6¾ in.)
Inscribed at lower right: *Degas*
2398

Provenance: Antonin Proust, Paris; Knoedler, Paris; César de Hauke,
New York; Andrew W. Mellon, Washington; Ailsa Mellon Bruce, New York,
1930.

Exhibitions: New York, Wildenstein "Degas," 1960, no. 25, repr.;
San Francisco 1961, no. 19, repr.; NGA 1966, no. 53, repr.

Bibliography: P. A. Lemoisne, *Degas et son oeuvre,* vol. 2, Paris, 1946, p. 236,
no. 432, repr. p. 237; F. Russoli and F. Minervino, *L'Opera completa di Degas,*
Milan, 1970, p. 110, no. 501, repr.; J. Clay, *L'Impressionisme,* Paris, 1971,
p. 68, repr. (color) p. 68; NGA 1975, p. 100, no. 2398, repr. p. 101; Walker
1975, repr. (color) p. 483, no. 716.

Edgar Degas, 1834-1917

Ballet Dancers, c.1877

Pastel and gouache, 0.297 x 0.269 (11¾ x 10⅝ in.)
Inscribed at lower left: *Degas*
2399

Provenance: Arnold & Tripp, Paris, 1881; Heber R. Bishop, New York (sale, New York, American Art Association, Jan. 20, 1906, no. 13); Durand-Ruel, New York, 1906; M. Rosenberg, Paris, 1908; César de Hauke, New York; Edward Molyneux, Paris; Ailsa Mellon Bruce, New York, 1955.

Exhibitions: Paris, Charpentier, "Danse et divertissements"; Molyneux 1952; New York, Wildenstein, "Degas," 1960, no. 27, repr.; San Francisco 1951, no. 17, repr.; NGA 1966, no. 52, repr.

Bibliography: P. A. Lemoisne, *Degas et son oeuvre,* vol. 2, Paris, 1946, p. 266, no. 481, repr. p. 267; F. Russoli and F. Minervino, *L'Opera completa di Degas,* Milan, 1970, p. 111, no. 531, repr.; NGA 1975, p. 100, no. 2399, repr. p. 101; Walker 1975, repr. (color) p. 483, no. 717.

Claude Monet, 1840-1926

Argenteuil, 1872

Canvas, 0.504 x 0.652 (19⅞ x 25⅝ in.)
Inscribed at lower right: *Claude Monet*
2414

Provenance: Mlle Marguerite Hugo, Paris, c.1957; Wildenstein, New York;
Ailsa Mellon Bruce, New York, 1966.

Exhibitions: Edinburgh, Royal Scottish Academy, and London, Tate Gallery,
"Monet," 1957, no. 32, pl. 24d.

Bibliography: L. Rossi Bortolatto, *L'Opera completa di Claude Monet,* 1870-1889,
Milan, 1972, p. 93, no. 66, repr. p. 92; D. Wildenstein, *Claude Monet,*
Biographie et catalogue raisonné, Lausanne-Paris, 1974, p. 210, no. 223, repr.
p. 211; NGA 1975, p. 244, no. 2414, repr. p. 245; Walker 1975, repr.
(color) p. 491, no. 731.

Claude Monet, 1840-1926

Ships Riding on the Seine at Rouen, 1872

Canvas, 0.378 x 0.466 (14⅞ x 18⅜ in.)
Inscribed at lower left: *Claude Monet*
2415

Provenance: Ernest Hoschedé, Paris (sale, Paris, Hôtel Drouot, June 5-6, 1878, no. 48); A. Dachery, Paris (sale, Paris, Hôtel Drouot, May 30, 1899, no. 40); Ernest Cognacq, Paris; Gabriel Cognacq (sale, Paris, Charpentier, May 14, 1952, no. 49, pl. 49); Edward Molyneux, Paris; Ailsa Mellon Bruce, New York, 1955.

Exhibitions: Paris, Musée de l'Orangerie, "Centenaire Monet-Rodin," 1940, no. 1; San Francisco 1961, no. 28, repr.; NGA 1966, no. 82, repr.

Bibliography: K. Kuh, "Golden Loans for a Silver Anniversary," *Saturday Review*, Mar. 19, 1966, repr. (color) p. 48; M. Bodelsen, "Early Impressionist Sales 1874-94 in the Light of Some Unpublished 'procès-verbaux'," *The Burlington Magazine* 110 (June, 1968): 340; D. Wildenstein, *Claude Monet, Biographie et catalogue raisonné*, vol. 1, Lausanne-Paris, 1974, p. 206, no. 210, repr. p. 207; NGA 1975, p. 244, no. 2415, repr. p. 245; Walker 1975, repr. (color) p. 491, no. 732.

Odilon Redon, 1840-1916

Flowers in a Vase, c. 1910

Canvas, 0.559 x 0.394 (22 x 15½ in.)
Inscribed at lower right: ODILON REDON
2428

Provenance: Private collection, Paris; Wildenstein, New York; Ailsa Mellon Bruce, New York, 1966.

Exhibitions: London, Matthiesen, "Odilon Redon," 1959, no. 69, repr.

Bibliography: NGA 1975, p. 284, no. 2428, repr. p. 285; Walker 1975, repr. (color) p. 518, no. 782.

Berthe Morisot, 1841-1895

The Artist's Sister at a Window, 1869

Canvas, 0.548 x 0.463 (21⅝ x 26¾ in.)
2419

Provenance: Mme Edma Morisot Pontillon, Paris; Mme Blanche Pontillon Forget, Paris; Mme Ernest Rouart, 1945; Edward Molyneux, Paris; Ailsa Mellon Bruce, New York, 1955.

Exhibitions: Paris, Salon, Société des artistes français, 1870, no. 2040; Paris, Bernheim-Jeune, "Cent oeuvres de Berthe Morisot," 1919, no. 6; Paris, Musée de l'Orangerie, "Berthe Morisot," (preface by Paul Valéry), 1941, no. 7; Paris, Durand-Ruel, "Quelques toiles importantes de collections particulières des XIX et XX siècles," 1945, no. 28; Paris, André Weil, "Berthe Morisot," 1947; Copenhagen, Ny-Carlsberg Glyptotek, "Berthe Morisot," 1949, no. 2, pl. I London, Arts Council of Great Britain, "Berthe Morisot," 1950, no. 2, pl. I; Molyneux 1952, repr.; San Francisco 1961, no. 30, repr.; NGA 1966, no. 93, repr.

Bibliography: T. Duret, *Histoire des peintres impressionistes*, Paris, 1906, pp. 161f; M. Angoulvent, *Berthe Morisot*, Paris, 1931, pp. 36, 118, no. 23; D. Rouart, *Correspondance de Berthe Morisot*, Paris, 1950, pp. 36f; A.M. F[rankfurter], "The Molyneux Collection Travels," *Art News* 51, no. 2 (Apr. 1952): 34, repr. p. 34; M.-L. Bataille and G. Wildenstein, *Berthe Morisot*, Paris, 1961, p. 24, no. 18, pl. 14; J. Rewald, *The History of Impressionism*, New York, 1961, 1973, pp. 241f; NGA 1975, p. 248, no. 2419, repr. p. 249; Walker 1975, repr. (color) p. 462, no. 674.

Berthe Morisot, 1841-1895

The Harbor at Lorient, 1869

Canvas, 0.435 x 0.730 (17⅛ x 28¾ in.)
Inscribed at lower right: *B Morisot*
2420

Provenance: Edouard Manet, gift from the artist, 1869; Gabriel Thomas, Paris,
by 1896; Mme Gabriel Thomas, Bellevue (S.-et-O.); Edward Molyneux,
Paris; Ailsa Mellon Bruce, New York, 1955.

Exhibitions: Paris, Nadar, "Première exposition, Société anonyme des artistes
peintres, sculpteurs, graveurs," 1874, no. 107 (*Marine*); Brussels, "La Libre
esthétique," 1894, probably no. 323 (*Marine*); Paris, Durand-Ruel, "Berthe
Morisot," (preface by Stéphane Mallarmé), 1896, no. 149; Paris, Bernheim-
Jeune, "Cent oeuvres de Berthe Morisot," 1919, no. 4; Pittsburgh, Carnegie
Institute, "Edouard Manet, Pierre Renoir, Berthe Morisot," 1924, no. 2;
Paris, Bernheim-Jeune, "Exposition d'oeuvres de Berthe Morisot," 1929,
no. 68; London, Royal Academy of Arts, "Masterpieces of French Art," 1932,
no. 460, pl. 122; Brussels, Palais des Beaux-Arts, "L'Impressionisme," 1935,
no. 53; Paris, Paul Rosenberg, "Exposition 'Le grand siècle'," 1936, no. 40;
London, New Burlington Galleries, Anglo French Art and Travel Society,
"Exhibition of Masters of French 19th Century Painting," 1936, no. 40; Paris,
Palais National des Arts, "Chefs-d'oeuvres de l'art français," 1937, no. 381;
Amsterdam, Stedelijk Museum, "Honderd Jaar Fransche Kunst," 1938,
no. 184, repr.; Molyneux 1952; Washington, D.C., National Gallery of Art,
"Masterpieces of Impressionist and Post-Impressionist Painting," 1959, repr.
p. 45; San Francisco 1961, no. 33, repr.; NGA 1966, no. 95, color repr.

Bibliography: A. Fourreau, *Berthe Morisot*, Paris, 1925, p. 32, pl. 1, and in New
York edition, 1925, pp. 34f., pl. 1; P. Jamot, "Etudes sur Manet," *Gazette des
Beaux-Arts* 15, Ser. 5, 1927, I, p. 29; M. Angoulvent, *Berthe Morisot*, Paris,
1931, pp. 29, 118, no. 19; L. Rouart, *Berthe Morisot*, Paris, 1941, repr. p. 12;
J. Rewald, *The History of Impressionism*, New York, 1949, p. 188, repr. p. 190;
1961, 1973, p. 222, repr. (color) p. 227; D. Rouart, *Correspondance de Berthe
Morisot*, Paris, 1950, pp. 33, 35; M.-L. Bataille and G. Wildenstein, *Berthe
Morisot*, Paris, 1961, p. 24, no. 17, pl. 13; H. Comstock, "The Connoisseur
in America: An Intimate View of French Masters," *The Connoisseur* 148,
no. 598 (Dec., 1961): repr. p. 338; R. Goldwater, "The Glory that was
France," *Art News* 65, no. 1 (Mar., 1966): 86, repr. (color) p. 44; M.H.
Young, "The Mellon Collections: The Great Years of French Painting," *Apollo*
83, no. 3 (June, 1966): 428, repr. (color) p. 431; H. Adhémar and S. Gache,
"L'Exposition de 1874 chez Nadar," *Centenaire de l'Impressionisme*, Paris, 1974,
p. 245, no. 107 (*Marine*); NGA 1975, p. 248, no. 2420, repr. p. 249; Walker
1975, repr. (color) p. 463, no. 675; Kelder 1977, p. 20, repr. (color) p. 21.

Auguste Renoir, 1841-1919

Head of a Dog, c.1870

Canvas, 0.219 x 0.200 (8⅝ x 7⅞ in.)
Inscribed at lower left: *.Renoir.*
2429

Provenance: Edward Molyneux, Paris; Ailsa Mellon Bruce, New York, 1955.

Exhibitions: Molyneux 1952; San Francisco 1961, no. 45, repr.; NGA 1966, no. 100, repr.

Bibliography: A. Vollard, *Tableaux, pastels & dessins de Pierre-Auguste Renoir*, vol. 1, Paris, 1918, repr. p. 16, no. 61; NGA 1975, p. 296, no. 2429, repr. p. 297; Walker 1975, repr. (color) p. 474, no. 702.

Auguste Renoir, 1841-1919

Regatta at Argenteuil, 1874

Canvas, 0.324 x 0.456 (12¾ x 18 in.)
2431

Provenance: Edward Molyneux, Paris; Ailsa Mellon Bruce, New York, 1955.

Exhibitions: Paris, Charpentier, "Paysages d'eau douce," 1945, no. 117, repr.;
Molyneux 1952; NGA 1966, no. 101, repr.

Bibliography: J. Rewald, *The History of Impressionism,* New York, 1961, 1973, repr.
p. 348; NGA 1975, p. 298, no. 2431, repr. p. 299; Walker 1975, repr.
(color) p. 474, no. 700.

Auguste Renoir, 1841-1919

Madame Monet and Her Son, 1874

Canvas, 0.504 x 0.680 (19⅞ x 26¾ in.)
2432

Provenance: The artist; Claude Monet, Giverny; Michel Monet, Giverny; Edward Molyneux, Paris; Ailsa Mellon Bruce, New York, 1955.

Exhibitions: Paris, Bernheim-Jeune, "Renoir," 1913, no. 6, repr. opp. p. 2 (*Dans l'herbe*); Paris, Musée de l'Orangerie, "Renoir," 1933, no. 20; Molyneux 1952, repr.; San Francisco 1961, no. 53, repr.; New York, Knoedler, "Impressionist Treasures from Private Collections in New York," 1966, no. 31, repr. p. 39; NGA 1966, no. 99, repr.

Bibliography: H. Graber, *Auguste Renoir,* Basel, 1943, p. 48, repr. p. 67; J. Rewald, *The History of Impressionism,* New York, 1946, p. 276, repr. p. 277; 1961, 1973, pp. 341f, repr. p. 343; A.M. F[rankfurter], "The Molyneux Collection Travels," *Art News* 51, no. 2 (Apr., 1952): repr. p. 34; P. Pool, *Impressionism,* London, 1967, repr. p. 160; J. Rewald, "How New York Became the Capital of 19th-century Paris," *Art News* 64, no. 9 (Jan., 1966): 36, repr. p. 35; P. Howard-Johnston, "Une visite à Giverny en 1924," *L'Oeil,* no. 171 (Mar., 1969): repr. p. 33; Réalités-Hachette, ed., *Renoir,* Paris, 1970, p. 81, repr. p. 80; F. Daulte, *Auguste Renoir, Catalogue raisonné de l'oeuvre peint,* vol. 1, Lausanne, 1971, no. 104, repr.; J. Clay, *L'Impressionisme,* Paris, 1971, repr. (color) p. 74; E. Fezzi, *L'Opera completa di Renoir nel periodo impressionista, 1869-1883,* Milan, 1972, p. 94, no. 123, repr. p. 95; NGA 1975, p. 298, no. 2432, repr. p. 299; Walker 1975, repr. (color) p. 468, no. 688.

Auguste Renoir, 1841-1919

Georges Rivière, 1877

Tile, 0.368 x 0.293 (14½ x 11½ in.)
Inscribed at lower left: *Renoir.77*
2436

Provenance: Georges Rivière, Paris; Edward Molyneux, Paris; Ailsa Mellon Bruce, New York, 1955.

Exhibitions: Molyneux 1952; Palm Beach 1958, no. 36; San Francisco 1961, no. 48, repr.; NGA 1966, no. 103, repr.

Bibliography: M. Berr de Turique, *Renoir,* Paris [1953], pl. 23 (color); F. Daulte, *Auguste Renoir, Catalogue raisonné de l'oeuvre peint,* vol. 1, Lausanne, 1971, no. 259, repr.; E. Fezzi, *L'opera completa di Renoir nel periodo impressionista,* 1867-1883, Milan, 1972, p. 102, no. 301, repr. p. 102; NGA 1975, p. 298, no. 2436, repr. p. 299; Walker 1975, repr. (color) p. 474, no. 703.

Auguste Renoir, 1841-1919

Landscape between Storms, 1874/75

Canvas 0.244 x 0.327 (9⅝ x 12⅞ in.)
Inscribed at lower left: *renoir*
2437

Provenance: Edward Molyneux, Paris; Ailsa Mellon Bruce, New York, 1955.

Exhibitions: Molyneux 1952; Palm Beach 1958, no. 37; San Francisco 1961, no. 40, repr.

Bibliography: A. Vollard, *Tableaux, pastels & dessins de Pierre Auguste Renoir*, vol. 2, Paris, 1918, repr. p. 39; NGA 1975, p. 298, no. 2437, repr. p. 299.

Auguste Renoir, 1841-1919

Woman by a Fence, 1866

Canvas, 0.250 x 0.161 (9⅞ x 6⅜ in.)
Inscribed at lower left: AR.
2438

Provenance: Ambroise Vollard, Paris; Edward Molyneux, Paris; Ailsa Mellon Bruce, New York, 1955.

Exhibitions: Molyneux 1952; San Francisco 1961, no. 43, repr.

Bibliography: F. Daulte, *Auguste Renoir, Catalogue raisonné de l'oeuvre peint*, vol. 1, Lausanne, 1971, no. 21, repr.; NGA 1975, p. 298, no. 2438, repr. p. 299.

Auguste Renoir, 1841-1919

Woman Standing by a Tree, 1866

Canvas, 0.252 x 0.159 (9⅞ x 6¼ in.)
Inscribed at lower left: AR
2439

Provenance: Ambroise Vollard, Paris; Edward Molyneux, Paris; Ailsa Mellon Bruce, New York, 1955.

Exhibitions: Molyneux 1952; San Francisco 1961, no. 44, repr.

Bibliography: A. Vollard, *Tableaux, pastels & dessins de Pierre-Auguste Renoir,* vol. 1, Paris, 1918, repr. p. 6, no. 21 (dated 1870); F. Daulte, *Auguste Renoir, Catalogue raisonné de l'oeuvre peint,* vol. 1, Lausanne, 1971, no. 22, repr.; NGA 1975, p. 300, no. 2439, repr. p. 301; Walker 1975, repr. (color) p. 469, no. 690.

Auguste Renoir, 1841-1919

Woman in a Park, 1870

Canvas, 0.261 x 0.161 (10¼ x 6⅜ in.)
Inscribed at lower right: R
2440

Provenance: Ambroise Vollard, Paris; Edward Molyneux, Paris; Ailsa Mellon
Bruce, New York, 1955.

Exhibitions: Molyneux 1952; San Francisco 1961, no. 52, repr.

Bibliography: A. Vollard, *Tableaux, pastels & dessins de Pierre-Auguste Renoir,* vol. 1,
Paris, 1918, repr. p. 6, no. 21 (dated 1870); F. Daulte, *Auguste Renoir,*
Catalogue raisonné de l'oeuvre peint, vol. 1, Lausanne, 1971, no. 51, repr.; NGA
1975, p. 300, no. 2440, repr. p. 301.

Auguste Renoir, 1841-1919

Child with Blond Hair, 1895/1900

Canvas, 0.097 x 0.085 (3¾ x 3⅜ in.)
Inscribed at lower right: R
2441

Provenance: Edward Molyneux, Paris; Ailsa Mellon Bruce, New York, 1955.

Exhibitions: Molyneux 1952.

Bibliography: A. Vollard, *Tableaux, pastels & dessins de Pierre Auguste Renoir*, vol. 2, Paris, 1918, repr. p. 175; NGA 1975, p. 300, no. 2441, repr. p. 301; Walker 1975, repr. (color) p. 469, no. 692.

Auguste Renoir, 1841-1919

Child with Brown Hair, 1887/88

Canvas, 0.118 x 0.102 (4⅝ x 4 in.)
Inscribed at upper right: *renoir*
2442

Provenance: Ambroise Vollard, Paris; Edward Molyneux, Paris; Ailsa Mellon Bruce, New York, 1955.

Exhibitions: Molyneux 1952.

Bibliography: A. Vollard, *Tableaux, pastels & dessins de Pierre Auguste Renoir*, vol. 2, Paris, 1918, repr. p. 175; F. Daulte, *Auguste Renoir, Catalogue raisonné de l'oeuvre peint*, vol. 1, Lausanne, 1971, no. 512, repr.; NGA 1975, p. 300, no. 2442, repr. p. 301; Walker 1975, repr. (color) p. 469, no. 691.

Auguste Renoir, 1841-1919

Young Girl Reading, c.1888

Canvas, 0.156 x 0.112 (6⅛ x 4¾ in.)
Inscribed at lower left: R
2443

Provenance: Ambroise Vollard, Paris; Edward Molyneux, Paris; Ailsa Mellon Bruce, New York, 1955.

Exhibitions: Molyneux 1952; San Francisco 1961, no. 55, repr.

Bibliography: A. Vollard, *Tableaux, pastels & dessins de Pierre Auguste Renoir,* vol. 2, Paris, 1918, repr. p. 84; F. Daulte, *Auguste Renoir, Catalogue raisonné de l'oeuvre peint,* vol. 1, Lausanne, 1971, no. 527, repr.; NGA 1975, p. 300, no. 2443, repr. p. 301.

NOTE: A study for this painting was formerly in the collection of Mrs. Jules Fribourg, New York (Daulte, no. 529, *Jeune Fille Lisant*).

Auguste Renoir, 1841-1919

Landscape at Vétheuil, c.1890

Canvas, 0.115 x 0.165 (4½ x 6½ in.)
Inscribed at lower center: *renoir*
2444

Provenance: Edward Molyneux, Paris; Ailsa Mellon Bruce, New York, 1955.

Exhibitions: Molyneux 1952; Palm Beach 1958, no. 33; San Francisco 1961, no. 47, repr.

Bibliography: A. Vollard, *Tableaux, pastels & dessins de Pierre Auguste Renoir,* vol. 2, Paris, 1918, repr. p. 69; NGA 1975, p. 300, no. 2444, repr. p. 301; Walker 1975, repr. (color) p. 474, no. 701.

Auguste Renoir, 1841-1919

Nude, c.1887

Canvas, 0.133 x 0.103 (5⅛ x 4 in.)
Inscribed at lower right: R.
2445

Provenance: Ambroise Vollard, Paris; Edward Molyneux, Paris; Ailsa Mellon Bruce, New York, 1955.

Exhibitions: Molyneux 1952; Palm Beach 1958, no. 34(?); San Francisco 1961, no. 50, repr.

Bibliography: A. Vollard, *Tableaux, pastels & dessins de Pierre Auguste Renoir,* vol. 2, Paris, 1918, repr. p. 157; F. Daulte, *Auguste Renoir, Catalogue raisonné de l'oeuvre peint,* vol. 1, Lausanne, 1971, no. 417, repr.; NGA 1975, p. 300, no. 2445, repr. p. 301.

Auguste Renoir, 1841-1919

Nude with Figure in Background, c.1882

Canvas, 0.128 x 0.083 (5 x 3¼ in.)
Inscribed at lower right: *renoir.*
2446

Provenance: Ambroise Vollard, Paris; Edward Molyneux, Paris; Ailsa Mellon Bruce, New York, 1955.

Exhibitions: Molyneux 1952; Palm Beach 1958, no. 34 (?); San Francisco 1961, no. 51, repr.

Bibliography: A. Vollard, *Tableaux, pastels & dessins de Pierre Auguste Renoir,* vol. 2, Paris, 1918, repr. p. 74; F. Daulte, *Auguste Renoir, Catalogue raisonné de l'oeuvre peint,* vol. 1, Lausanne, 1971, no. 416, repr.; NGA 1975, p. 300, no. 2446, repr. p. 301.

Auguste Renoir, 1841-1919

The Blue River, 1890/1900

Canvas, 0.080 x 0.096 (3⅛ x 3¾ in.)
Inscribed at lower right: *renoir*
2447

Provenance: Edward Molyneux, Paris; Ailsa Mellon Bruce, New York, 1955.

Exhibitions: Molyneux 1952; San Francisco 1961, no. 39, repr. (dated 1868).

Bibliography: A. Vollard, *Tableaux, pastels & dessins de Pierre Auguste Renoir*, vol. 2, Paris, 1918, repr. p. 135; NGA 1975, p. 302, no. 2447, repr. p. 303.

Auguste Renoir, 1841-1919

Maison de la Poste, Cagnes, 1906/07

Canvas, 0.133 x 0.225 (5¼ x 8⅞ in.)
Inscribed at lower left: *Renoir.*
2449

Provenance: Durand-Ruel, Paris, 1912; Howard Pretzel, 1936; Edward
Molyneux, Paris; Ailsa Mellon Bruce, New York, 1955.

Exhibitions: Molyneux 1952; San Francisco 1961, no. 54, repr.

Bibliography: NGA 1975, p. 302, no. 2449, repr. p. 303.

Auguste Renoir, 1841-1919

Jeanne Samary, 1878

Canvas, 0.191 x 0.181 (7½ x 7⅛ in.)
Inscribed at upper left with monogram: AR
2450

Provenance: Paul Lagarde, Paris; Edward Molyneux, Paris; Ailsa Mellon Bruce, New York, 1955.

Exhibitions: Molyneux 1952; Palm Beach 1958, no. 35; San Francisco 1961, no. 49, repr.

Bibliography: A. Vollard, *Tableaux, pastels et dessins de Pierre Auguste Renoir,* vol. 2, Paris, 1918, repr. p. 110; F. Daulte, *Auguste Renoir, Catalogue raisonné de l'oeuvre peint,* vol. 1, Lausanne, 1971, no. 264, repr.; NGA 1975, p. 302, no. 2450, repr. p. 303.

Auguste Renoir, 1841-1919

Peaches on a Plate, 1902/05

Canvas, 0.222 x 0.356 (8¾ x 14 in.)
Atelier stamp at lower left: *Renoir*
2451

Provenance: Sam Salz, New York; Ailsa Mellon Bruce, New York, 1958.

Exhibitions: San Francisco 1961, no. 46, repr.

Bibliography: NGA 1975, p. 302, no. 2451, repr. p. 303.

Vincent van Gogh, Dutch, 1853-1890

Farmhouse in Provence, Arles, 1888

Canvas, 0.461 x 0.609 (18⅛ x 24 in.)
2406

Provenance: Mrs. J. van Gogh-Bonger, Amsterdam; Gaston Bernheim de Villers, Paris; Reid & Lefevre, London; Ackermann, Paris; Edward Molyneux, Paris; Ailsa Mellon Bruce, New York, 1955.

Exhibitions: Amsterdam, Stedelijk Museum, "Tentoonstelling van schilderijen van Gogh," 1905, no. 111; Paris, Bernheim-Jeune, "L'Epoque française de van Gogh," 1927 (no catalogue); Molyneux 1952, repr.; San Francisco 1961, no. 65, repr.; NGA 1966, no. 131, repr.

Bibliography: T. Duret, *Vincent van Gogh,* Paris, 1916, pl. 26; J. & G. Bernheim-Jeune, *L'Art moderne et quelques aspects de l'art d'autrefois,* vol. 1, Paris, 1919, pl. 65; J.-B. de La Faille, *L'Oeuvre de Vincent van Gogh,* vol. 1, Paris and Brussels, 1928, p. 160, no. 565, vol. 2, pl. CLVI, no. 565; W. Scherjon and J. de Gruyter, *Vincent van Gogh's Great Period,* Amsterdam, 1937, repr. p. 187, no. 170; J.-B. de La Faille, *Vincent van Gogh,* Paris, 1939, no. 542, repr. p. 381; A.M. F[rankfurter], "The Molyneux Collection Travels," *Art News* 51, no. 2 (Apr. 1952): p. 34; J.-B. de La Faille, *The Works of Vincent van Gogh,* Amsterdam, 1970, no. 565, repr. p. 237; NGA 1975, p. 156, no. 2406, repr. p. 157; Walker 1975, repr. (color) p. 525, no. 791.

Georges Seurat, 1859-1891

Study for "La Grande Jatte," 1884/85

Wood, 0.159 x 0.250 (6¼ x 9⅞ in.)
Stamp at lower left: *Seurat*
2453

Provenance: Bernheim-Jeune, Paris; Lefevre, London; Percy Moore Turner, London, by 1933; Wildenstein, London; Edward Molyneux, Paris, 1943; Ailsa Mellon Bruce, New York, 1955.

Exhibitions: Paris, Galerie des Beaux-Arts, "Seurat et ses amis," 1933-34, no. 67; Paris, Bernheim-Jeune, "Quelques tableaux d'Ingres à Gauguin," 1935, no. 29 or 30; London, Wildenstein, "Seurat and His Contemporaries," 1937, no. 39; Molyneux 1952; San Francisco 1961, no. 57, repr.; NGA 1966, no. 145, repr.

Bibliography: C. Zervos, "Un Dimanche à La Grande Jatte et la technique de Seurat," *Cahiers d'Art* 3, no. 9 (1928), repr. p. 364; D.C. Rich, *Seurat and the Evolution of "La Grande Jatte,"* Chicago, 1935, p. 55, no. 23, pl. XXII; J. de Laprade, *Seurat,* Monaco, 1945, pl. 27; H. Dorra and J. Rewald, *Seurat,* Paris, 1959, p. 116, no. 109, repr.; C.M. de Hauke, *Seurat et son oeuvre,* vol. 1, Paris, 1961, p. 68, no. 110, repr. p. 69; NGA 1975, p. 324, no. 2453, repr. p. 325; Walker 1975, repr. (color) p. 519, no. 786.

Henri de Toulouse-Lautrec, 1864-1901

The Artist's Dog Flèche, 1880

Wood, 0.234 x 0.141 (9¼ x 5½ in.)
Inscribed at lower right: HTL (in monogram) LA FLECHE
2456

Provenance: André Weil, Paris; Edward Molyneux, Paris; Ailsa Mellon Bruce, New York, 1955.

Exhibitions: Molyneux 1952; NGA 1966, no. 147, repr.

Bibliography: M.G. Dortu, *Toulouse-Lautrec et son oeuvre*, vol. 2, New York, 1971, p. 64, no. P.141, repr. p. 65; NGA 1975, p. 350, no. 2456, repr. p. 351; Walker 1975, repr. (color) p. 537, no. 811.

Henri de Toulouse-Lautrec, 1864-1901

Carmen Gaudin, 1885

Wood, 0.238 x 0.149 (9⅜ x 5⅞ in.)
2457

Provenance: François Gauzi, Toulouse; Durand-Matthiesen, Geneva; Edward Molyneux, Paris; Ailsa Mellon Bruce, New York, 1955.

Exhibitions: Toulouse, Palais de Télégramme, "Toulouse-Lautrec, Rétrospective," 1907; London, Matthiesen, "Toulouse-Lautrec," 1951, no. 4, repr.; Molyneux 1952; San Francisco 1961, no. 61, repr.; NGA 1966, no. 148, repr.

Bibliography: J. Pigasse, *Toulouse-Lautrec,* 1907, pp. 20, 27; M. Joyant, *Henri de Toulouse-Lautrec,* vol. 1, Paris, 1926, p. 260; P. de Lapparent, *Toulouse-Lautrec,* Paris, 1927, pp. 15, 21, 47; M.G. Dortu, *Toulouse-Lautrec,* Paris, 1952, p. 5; F. Gauzi, *Lautrec et son temps,* Paris, 1954, p. 130, n. 1; H. Perruchot, *La vie de Toulouse-Lautrec,* Paris, 1958, p. 116; G. Caproni, *L'Opera completa di Toulouse-Lautrec,* Milan, 1969, p. 98, no. 173; M.G. Dortu, *Toulouse-Lautrec et son oeuvre,* vol. 2, New York, 1971, p. 106, no. P.244, repr. p. 107; NGA 1975, p. 352, no. 2457, repr. p. 353; Walker 1975, repr. (color) p. 533, no. 805.

Pierre Bonnard, 1867-1947

Two Dogs in a Deserted Street, c.1893

Wood, 0.315 x 0.270 (13⅞ x 10⅝ in.)
Inscribed at lower right: *Bonnard*
2375

Provenance: Thadée Natanson, Paris (sale, Paris, Hôtel Drouot, June 13, 1908, no. 9); Bernheim-Jeune, Paris; Edward Molyneux, Paris; Ailsa Mellon Bruce, New York, 1955.

Exhibitions: Paris, Durand-Ruel, "Exposition P. Bonnard," 1896, no. 45 (*Une Rue à Eragny*); Paris, Bernheim-Jeune, "La Faune," 1910, no. 49; Paris, Musée de l'Orangerie, "Bonnard," 1947, no. 7; New York, The Museum of Modern Art, and The Cleveland Museum of Art, "Pierre Bonnard," 1948, no. 5, repr. p. 66; Paris, Bernheim-Jeune, "Exposition rétrospective Bonnard," 1950, no. 1, repr.; Molyneux 1952; San Francisco 1961, no. 1, repr.; NGA 1966, no. 54, repr.

Bibliography: L. Werth, *Bonnard,* Paris, 1919, pl. 6; T. Klingsor, "Pierre Bonnard," *L'Amour de l'art* 2 (Aug. 8, 1921): 246; G. Coquiot, *Bonnard,* Paris, 1922, pp. 21, 23; *Le Point* 3, no. 15 (June 1938): repr. p. 99; G. Besson, *Bonnard,* Paris, 1947, pl. 16; C. Terrasse, Preface to Bernheim-Jeune catalogue, 1950, p. 15; T. Natanson, *Le Bonnard que je propose,* Geneva, 1951, pp. 114, 236; H. Rumpel, *Pierre Bonnard,* Bern, 1952, p. 21, pl. 11; A. Terrasse, *Bonnard,* Geneva, 1964, repr. (color) p. 31; J. and H. Dauberville, *Bonnard,* vol. 1, Paris, 1965, p. 129, no. 63, repr. p. 128, repr. (color) p. 128 bis; A. Terrasse, *Pierre Bonnard,* Paris, 1967, repr. (color) p. 47; A. Fermigier, *Pierre Bonnard,* New York, 1969, repr. p. 15; NGA 1975, p. 32, no. 2375, repr. p. 33; Walker 1975, repr. (color) p. 581, no. 886.

Pierre Bonnard, 1867-1947

The Cab Horse, c.1895

Wood, 0.297 x 0.400 (11¾ x 15¾ in.)
Inscribed at lower right: *Bonnard*
2376

Provenance: Shchukin, Moscow; Bernheim-Jeune, Paris, 1899; Private
Collection, New York; Edward Molyneux, Paris; Ailsa Mellon Bruce,
New York, 1955.

Exhibitions: Paris, Bernheim-Jeune, "XXXIV Peintures de Pierre Bonnard," 1946,
no. 3; Paris, Musée de l'Orangerie, "Bonnard," 1947, no. 10 (*Le cheval de
fiacre*); New York, The Museum of Modern Art, and The Cleveland Museum
of Art, "Pierre Bonnard," 1948, no. 6, repr. p. 68; Molyneux 1952, repr.;
Palm Beach, The Society of the Four Arts, "Loan Exhibition of Works by
Pierre Bonnard," 1957, no. 4; Palm Beach 1958, no. 25, repr.; San Francisco
1961, no. 4, repr.; New York, The Museum of Modern Art, Chicago, The
Art Institute of Chicago, Los Angeles County Museum of Art, "Bonnard and
His Environment," 1964-65, no. 12 (*Boulevard des Batignolles*), repr. (color)
p. 68; NGA 1966, no. 155, repr.; New York, Christie's, "Van Gogh,
Gauguin and Their Circle," 1968, no. 37, repr.

Bibliography: C. Terrasse, *Bonnard*, Paris, 1927, repr. p. 73; René-Marie,
"Bonnard et son époque," *Le Point* 24 (1943): repr. p. 28; L. Werth,
T. Natanson, L. Gischia, G. Diehl, *Pierre Bonnard*, Paris, 1945, repr. p. 9;
F.-J. Beer, *Bonnard*, Marseille, 1947, repr. (color) pl. I; T. Natanson,
Le Bonnard que je propose, Geneva, 1951, pl. 3; H. Rumpel, *Pierre Bonnard*, Bern,
1952, pl. 5; P. Courthion, *Paris des temps nouveaux*, Geneva, 1957, repr. (color)
p. 65; A. Terrasse, *Bonnard*, Geneva, 1964, pp. 32, 94, repr. (color) p. 29;
J. and H. Dauberville, *Bonnard*, vol. 1 Paris, 1965, p. 148, no. 92 bis, repr.
p. 148, repr. (color) p. 148 *bis*; K. Kuh, "Golden Loans for a Silver
Anniversary," *Saturday Review*, Mar. 19, 1966, repr. p. 51; A. Terrasse, *Pierre
Bonnard*, Paris, 1967, repr. (color) p. 42; A. Fermigier, *Bonnard*, New York,
1969, p. 20, repr. p. 16; NGA 1975, p. 32, no. 2376, repr. p. 33; Walker
1975, repr. (color) p. 580, no. 885.

Pierre Bonnard, 1867-1947

Children Leaving School, c. 1895

Cardboard on wood, 0.289 x 0.440 (11⅜ x 17⅜ in.)
Inscribed at lower right: *Bonnard*
2377

Provenance: The artist; Bernheim-Jeune, Paris, 1912; Private Collection, 1947;
Edward Molyneux, Paris; Ailsa Mellon Bruce, New York, 1955.

Exhibitions: Paris, Bernheim-Jeune, "XXXIV Peintures de Pierre Bonnard," 1946,
no. 1; Paris, Musée de l'Orangerie, "Exposition Bonnard," 1947, no. 9;
Molyneux 1952; New Haven, Yale University Art Gallery, "Pictures
Collected by Yale Alumni," 1956, no. 131, repr.; San Francisco 1961, no. 2,
repr.; New York, The Museum of Modern Art, Chicago, The Art Institute of
Chicago, Los Angeles County Museum of Art, "Bonnard and His
Environment," 1964-65, no. 4, repr. p. 30.

Bibliography: L. Werth, *Bonnard*, Paris, 1919, pl. 3; E. Faure, *Histoire de l'art
moderne*, vol. 4, Paris, 1921, repr. p. 451; G. Coquiot, *Bonnard*, Paris, 1922,
p. 48; C. Terrasse, *Bonnard*, Paris, 1927, p. 42, repr. p. 41; G. Besson, *La
Peinture française au XIX siècle*, vol. 3, Paris, 1934, pl. 9; G. Besson, "Pierre
Bonnard," *Arts de France* 4 (Mar. 15, 1946): repr. p. 12; J. and H. Dauberville,
Bonnard, vol. 1, Paris, 1965, p. 200, no. 174, repr.; A. Terrasse, *Pierre Bonnard*,
Paris, 1967, repr. p. 38; A. Fermigier, *Pierre Bonnard*, New York, 1969, p. 20,
repr. p. 15; NGA 1975, p. 34, no. 2377, repr. p. 35; Walker 1975, repr.
(color) p. 581, no. 888.

Pierre Bonnard, 1867-1947

The Artist's Sister and Her Children, 1898

Cardboard on wood, 0.305 x 0.254 (12 x 10 in.)
Inscribed at upper left: *98 Bonnard*
2378

Provenance: Alfred Daber, Paris, 1933; George Renand, Paris; Edward
Molyneux, Paris; Ailsa Mellon Bruce, New York, 1955.

Exhibitions: Paris, Musée de l'Orangerie, "Bonnard," 1947, no. 12; Paris,
Bernheim-Jeune, "Exposition rétrospective Bonnard," 1950, no. 3; Molyneux
1952; Palm Beach, The Society of the Four Arts, "Loan Exhibition of Works
by Pierre Bonnard," 1957, no. 2; Palm Beach 1958, no. 24; San Francisco
1961, no. 3, repr.; New York, The Museum of Modern Art, Chicago, The
Art Institute of Chicago, Los Angeles County Museum of Art, "Bonnard and
His Environment," 1964-65, no. 9, repr. p. 33; NGA 1966, no. 157, repr.

Bibliography: F.-J. Beer, *Bonnard*, Marseille, 1947, p. 52, fig. 32; M. Raynal,
History of Modern Painting, From Baudelaire to Bonnard, vol. 1, Geneva, 1949, repr.
(color) p. 103; J. and H. Dauberville, *Bonnard*, vol. 1, Paris, 1965, p. 203,
no. 181, repr. p. 203; NGA 1975, p. 34, no. 2378, repr. p. 35; Walker
1975, repr. (color) p. 580, no. 884.

Edouard Vuillard, 1868-1940

Child Wearing a Red Scarf, c.1891

Cardboard on wood, 0.292 x 0.175 (11½ x 6⅞ in.)
Atelier stamp at upper right: *E Vuillard*
2462

Provenance: Edward Molyneux, Paris; Ailsa Mellon Bruce, New York, 1955.

Exhibitions: Paris, Charpentier, "Vuillard," 1948 (not in catalogue); Molyneux 1952; Palm Beach 1958, no. 43; San Francisco 1961, no. 69, repr.; NGA 1966, no. 171, repr.

Bibliography: J. Clay, *L'Impressionisme,* Paris, 1971, p. 263, repr. (color) p. 263; NGA 1975, p. 370, no. 2462, repr. p. 371; Walker 1975, repr. (color) p. 585, no. 895.

Edouard Vuillard, 1868-1940

Woman at Her Toilette, c. 1891

Cardboard on wood, 0.225 x 0.209 (8⅞ x 8¼ in.)
Atelier stamp at lower right: *E Vuillard*
2463

Provenance: Paul Pétridès, Paris; Edward Molyneux, Paris; Ailsa Mellon Bruce, New York, 1955.

Exhibitions: Molyneux 1952; Palm Beach 1958, no. 44; San Francisco 1961, no. 73, repr.; NGA 1966, no. 173, repr.

Bibliography: NGA 1975, p. 372, no. 2463, repr. p. 373.

Edouard Vuillard, 1868-1940

The Conversation, c. 1892

Canvas, 0.238 x 0.334 (9⅜ x 13⅛ in.)
Atelier stamp at lower left: *E Vuillard*
2464

Provenance: Tooth, London; Edward Molyneux, Paris, 1947; Ailsa Mellon Bruce, New York, 1955.

Exhibitions: Paris, Charpentier, "Vuillard," 1948, no. 9; Molyneux 1952; Palm Beach 1958, no. 45; San Francisco 1961, no. 71, repr.; NGA 1966, no. 174, repr.

Bibliography: A. Chastel, *Vuillard, Peintures 1890-1930*, Paris, 1948, repr. (color) pl. II; NGA 1975, p. 372, no. 2464, repr. p. 373.

Edouard Vuillard, 1868-1940

Woman in Black, c.1891

Cardboard, 0.268 x 0.219 (10½ x 8⅝ in.)
Atelier stamp at lower left: *E Vuillard*
2465

Provenance: Edward Molyneux, Paris; Ailsa Mellon Bruce, New York, 1955.

Exhibitions: Paris, Louis Carré, "Vuillard," 1942; Palm Beach 1958, no. 46; San Francisco 1961, no. 70, repr.; NGA 1966, no. 172, repr.

Bibliography: NGA 1975, p. 372, no. 2465, repr. p. 373.

Edouard Vuillard, 1868-1940

Two Women Drinking Coffee, c.1891

Cardboard on wood, 0.215 x 0.288 (8½ x 11⅜ in.)
2466

Provenance: Prince Antoine Bibesco, Paris; Edward Molyneux, Paris;
Ailsa Mellon Bruce, New York, 1955.

Exhibitions: Palm Beach 1958, no. 47; San Francisco 1961, no. 68, repr.; NGA
1966, no. 180, repr.

Bibliography: NGA 1975, p. 372, no. 2466, repr. p. 373.

Edouard Vuillard, 1868-1940

The Yellow Curtain, c.1893

Canvas, 0.349 x 0.390 (13¾ x 15⅜ in.)
Atelier stamp at lower left: *E Vuillard*
2467

Provenance: Edward Molyneux, Paris; Ailsa Mellon Bruce, New York, 1955.

Exhibitions: Paris, Charpentier, "Vuillard," 1948, no. 6; Molyneux 1952;
San Francisco 1961, no. 72, repr.; NGA 1966, no. 175, repr.

Bibliography: NGA 1975, p. 372, no. 2467, repr. p. 373; Walker 1975, repr.
(color) p. 585, no. 896.

Edouard Vuillard, 1868-1940

Woman Sitting by the Fireside, c.1894

Cardboard, 0.213 x 0.261 (8⅜ x 10¼ in.)
Inscribed at lower right: *E Vuillard*
2468

Provenance: Edward Molyneux, Paris; Ailsa Mellon Bruce, New York, 1955.

Exhibitions: Molyneux 1952; San Francisco 1961, no. 75, repr.; NGA 1966, no.179, repr.

Bibliography: NGA 1975, p. 372, no. 2468, repr. p. 373.

Edouard Vuillard, 1868-1940

Breakfast, 1894

Cardboard on wood, 0.269 x 0.229 (10⅝ x 9 in.)
Inscribed at lower left: *E Vuillard 94*
2469

Provenance: Valentine Gallery, New York (sale, New York, American Art Association, Mar. 24, 1932, no. 26); Captain Richard Peto, Isle of Wight; Reid & Lefevre, London, 1944; Edward Molyneux, Paris, 1945; Ailsa Mellon Bruce, New York, 1955.

Exhibitions: St. Louis, City Art Museum, "An Exhibition of Paintings & Prints by the Masters of Post-Impressionism," 1931, no. 42; Molyneux 1952; NGA 1966, no. 178, repr.

Bibliography: NGA 1975, p. 372, no. 2469, repr. p. 373.

Edouard Vuillard, 1868-1940

The Artist's Paint Box and Moss Roses, 1903

Cardboard, 0.361 x 0.429 (14¼ x 16⅞ in.)
Inscribed at lower left: *E Vuillard*
2470

Provenance: Bernheim-Jeune, Paris, 1903; Paul Rosenberg, Paris, 1904; Comte Isaac de Camondo, Paris; Bertrand, Paris; Wildenstein, New York; Ailsa Mellon Bruce, New York, 1959.

Exhibitions: San Francisco 1961, no. 74, repr.; New York, Wildenstein, "Vuillard," 1964, no. 19, repr.; NGA 1966, no. 176, repr.

Bibliography: J. Salomon, *Vuillard,* Paris, 1968, p. 156, repr. (color) p. 156; S. Preston, *Vuillard,* New York, 1972, p. 102, repr. (color) p. 103; NGA 1975, p. 374, no. 2470, repr. p. 375; Walker 1975, repr. (color) p. 584, no. 892.

Edouard Vuillard, 1868-1940

Vase of Flowers on a Mantlepiece, c.1904

Cardboard on wood, 0.362 x 0.295 (14¼ x 11⅝ in.)
Inscribed at upper right: *E Vuillard*
2471

Provenance: Prince Antoine Bibesco, Paris; Edward Molyneux, Paris; Ailsa Mellon Bruce, New York, 1955.

Exhibitions: Paris, Bernheim-Jeune, "Vuillard," Nov. 1908, no. 20; San Francisco 1961, no. 66, repr; NGA 1966, no. 186, repr.

Bibliography: J. Clay, *L'Impressionisme,* Paris, 1971, repr. (color) p. 218; NGA 1975, p. 374, no. 2471, repr. p. 375; Walker 1975, repr. (color) p. 584, no. 891.

Henri Matisse, 1869-1954

Still Life, c. 1905

Cardboard on wood, 0.170 x 0.248 (6¾ x 9¾ in.)
Inscribed at lower right: *Henri-Matisse*
2412

Provenance: Edward Molyneux, Paris; Ailsa Mellon Bruce, New York, 1955.

Exhibitions: Molyneux 1952; San Francisco 1961, no. 26, repr. (dated 1898); NGA 1966, no. 192, repr.

Bibliography: J. Leymarie, "Les deux horizons d'Henri Matisse," *Hommage à Matisse*, special issue of XXᵉ Siècle, Paris, 1970, repr. p. 30; NGA 1975, p. 228, no. 2412, repr. p. 229.

Georges Rouault, 1871-1958

Christ and the Doctor, c. 1935

Canvas, 0.087 x 0.108 (3⅜ x 4¼ in.)
Inscribed at lower left: *Rouault.*
2452

Provenance: Edward Molyneux, Paris; Ailsa Mellon Bruce, New York, 1955.

Exhibitions: Molyneux 1952; Palm Beach 1958, no. 38; San Francisco 1961, no. 56, repr.

Bibliography: NGA 1975, p. 310, no. 2452, repr. p. 311.

Maurice Utrillo, 1883-1955

Row of Houses at Pierrefitte, c.1905

Cardboard on wood, 0.239 x 0.342 (9⅜ x 13½ in.)
Inscribed at lower right: *Maurice Utrillo.V.*
2458

Provenance: Paul Pétridès, Paris; Edward Molyneux, Paris; Ailsa Mellon Bruce, New York, 1955.

Exhibitions: Molyneux 1952; Palm Beach 1958, no. 41 or 42; San Francisco 1961, no. 64, repr.; Pittsburgh, Carnegie Institute, "Maurice Utrillo," 1963, no. 1, repr.; NGA 1966, no. 198, repr.

Bibliography: P. Pétridès, *L'Oeuvre complet de Maurice Utrillo,* vol. 1, Paris, 1950, p. 64, no. 11, repr. p. 65; NGA 1975, p. 358, no. 2458, repr. p. 359.

Maurice Utrillo, 1883-1955

Landscape, Pierrefitte, c.1907

Cardboard on wood, 0.251 x 0.345 (9⅞ x 13⅝ in.)
Inscribed at lower right: *Maurice Utrillo.V.*
2459

Provenance: Edward Molyneux, Paris; Ailsa Mellon Bruce, New York, 1955.

Exhibitions: Molyneux 1952; Palm Beach 1958, no. 41 or 42; San Francisco 1961, no. 63, repr.; Pittsburgh, Carnegie Institute, "Maurice Utrillo," 1963, no. 3, repr.; NGA 1966, no. 199, repr.

Bibliography: NGA 1975, p. 358, no. 2459, repr. p. 359.

Index of Artists

Bonnard, Pierre 84–91

Boudin, Eugène 6–17

Corot, Jean-Baptiste-Camille 2–5

Degas, Edgar 24–29

Gogh, Vincent van 76

Manet, Edouard 20–23

Matisse, Henri 112

Monet, Claude 30–33

Morisot, Berthe 36–39

Pissarro, Camille 18

Redon, Odilon 34

Renoir, Auguste 40–75

Rouault, Georges 114

Seurat, Georges 78

Toulouse-Lautrec, Henri de 80–83

Utrillo, Maurice 116–119

Vuillard, Edouard 92–111